Series 654
A Ladybird Book

It is possible to enjoy riding a motor cycle or scooter without knowing anything about its mechanical details. However, understanding brings greater proficiency and safety, and the ability to cope with today's congested traffic conditions.

This well illustrated book will help both new and more experienced riders to understand their machines, and interest the many others who like to know how things work. It explains simply and clearly the operation of each part and ends with hints on safe riding and maintenance.

We wish to acknowledge the assistance of B.S.A. Motor Cycles Ltd. in the preparation of this book.

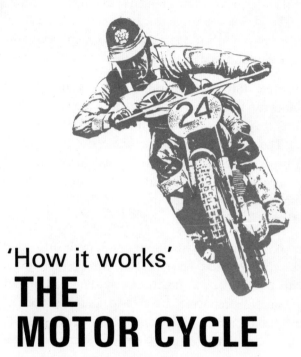

'How it works'
THE
MOTOR CYCLE

by DAVID CAREY
with illustrations by B. H. ROBINSON

Publishers : Wills & Hepworth Ltd., Loughborough
First published 1968   ©   *Printed in England*

Understanding the machine

It is possible to enjoy riding a motor cycle or scooter without knowing anything about its mechanical performance. The various controls can be operated quite satisfactorily even though the processes which make the machine respond remain a complete mystery.

However, this sort of riding has its drawbacks. Machines can be stubborn: on occasions they may refuse to start, they may run unevenly or break down altogether. The cure might be fairly simple, but if the works are a mystery you can be put to great inconvenience. Mechanical damage can be caused through inconsiderate use, and safety can be affected by lack of proper attention.

An understanding of how your motor cycle or scooter works brings positive benefits. You will be able to get the best out of it by sympathetic handling and proper care. You will frequently be able to find the cause of some trouble that may develop. Additionally, you will always have an interesting talking point when you meet other owners of similar or different models. As you compare the various technical features, you will become even more informed.

If you understand your machine and honour the Highway Code, you will find endless pleasure in riding proficiently and safely on the roads. This book is intended to help you achieve that satisfying result.

7214 0224 0

Operating the machine

In general terms, the operation of a lightweight motor cycle is very similar to that of a motor scooter and there are many examples of each type. Beginners are advised to start their riding on a machine they will be able to control easily: heavier and more powerful models are for the experts.

Pedal cycles, which most people have ridden at one time or another, require human effort to make them go. Motorised machines need no human effort. They simply require guidance and control.

The engine is started by exerting foot pressure on a lever. This is the *kick-starter*. There is a *clutch* lever on the handlebar to disengage the engine from the *transmission*; a twist-grip *accelerator* to control speed, and a gear-change pedal to select the various ratios in the *gearbox*. The front brake is applied by a hand lever and the rear brake by a pedal. You steer largely by leaning the machine to left or right depending on which way you wish to go.

Power is provided by the engine which is the most complicated part of the machine. It requires petrol and air to provide a *combustion mixture* and electricity to produce a spark which will make the mixture burn. The engine also needs oil to lubricate the working parts.

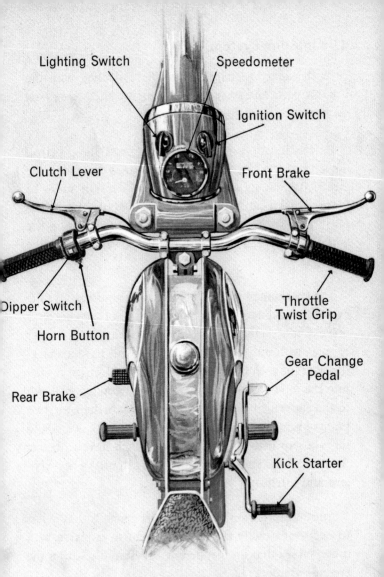

Controls of a Light Machine

The ignition system

In the next few pages we shall be dealing with the various parts and systems of the engine and seeing how each one does its job.

Before it can work, the engine must have petrol, air and electricity. The *ignition system* provides the electricity and its sole purpose is to cause a spark to jump across a gap between the *electrodes* of the *sparking plug*. This spark will ignite the fuel/air mixture in the engine cylinder and produce the power to run the machine.

The sparking plug is screwed into the engine above the cylinder or cylinders. Most lightweight motor cycles have one cylinder so they will have one sparking plug. Larger engines with more than one cylinder will have a sparking plug for each cylinder. High voltage electricity is fed into the top of the sparking plug and is conducted down to the end which is inside the engine. Here there are two points known as electrodes. An electric spark is made to jump a gap between these points which have to be set the correct distance apart to ensure a spark of the right size and intensity.

Another important feature of the spark is that it has to occur at exactly the right moment to coincide with other things that are happening very rapidly within the engine cylinder.

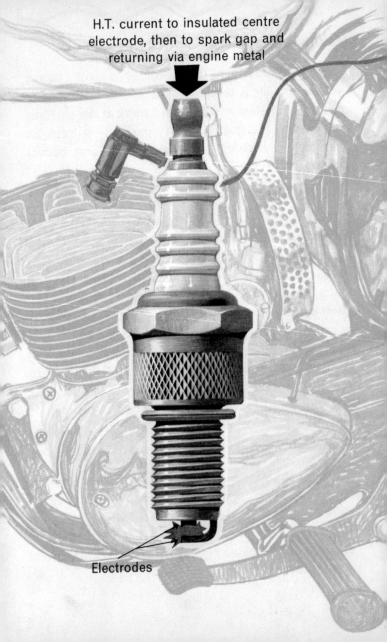

H.T. current to insulated centre electrode, then to spark gap and returning via engine metal

Electrodes

Making low voltage electricity

The main purpose of the electrical system of a motor cycle or scooter is to provide the necessary voltage to operate the ignition and produce a spark at the sparking plug points. It has a secondary purpose—to generate low voltage electricity for lights, horn and battery charging.

Machines can be of different size, type and age, and different kinds of electrical arrangements may be used. In the past, the flywheel magneto was the most popular but today, on nearly all new touring machines, electricity is generated by an *alternator*. This device consists of a stator, or casing, made up of laminated iron rings and containing six copper wire coils. A rotor, carrying six magnets and driven by the engine crankshaft, is positioned within the stator assembly. When the crankshaft revolves the rotor revolves with it, and the magnets spinning past the coils cause electricity to be generated. Three or four of the coils are connected to the ignition system while the others supply current for battery charging.

Alternators generate alternating (AC) current, that is, current that flows first in one direction then back again. This is suitable for ignition but for battery charging, direct (DC) current is necessary. A *rectifier* is therefore connected in the battery circuit, which makes the current flow in one direction only.

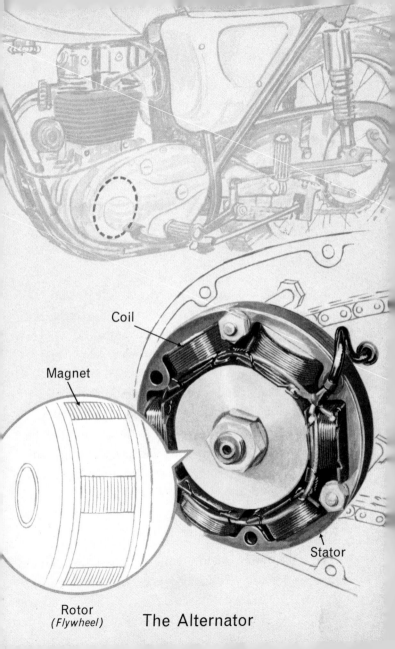

Coil

Magnet

Rotor
(Flywheel)

Stator

The Alternator

Making high voltage electricity

Low voltage electricity supplied by a battery, or generated in an alternator, normally measures six or twelve volts. This is sufficient for the general electrical equipment, but the sparking plug needs high voltage electricity to produce a satisfactory spark. In fact several thousand volts are required for this purpose. The big step-up of electrical pressure is obtained by means of an *ignition coil*. This was sometimes included in the magneto of small machines but more often a separate coil is now fitted.

The ignition coil actually consists of two coils of copper wire: the primary (thick wire) and the secondary (thin wire). The primary coil is fed with low voltage electricity from the alternator and when this low voltage current is interrupted it causes a very high voltage to be 'induced' in the secondary coil. The amount of increase in voltage is in proportion to the number of windings, or length of wire, in each coil. Thus, if for example the primary coil has seventy winds and the secondary coil has, say, seven thousand, the high voltage electricity leaving the ignition coil would be in the proportion of seventy to seven thousand, or one hundred times the low voltage electricity entering it.

The interruption of low voltage current mentioned above is effected by a *contact breaker* (see next chapter).

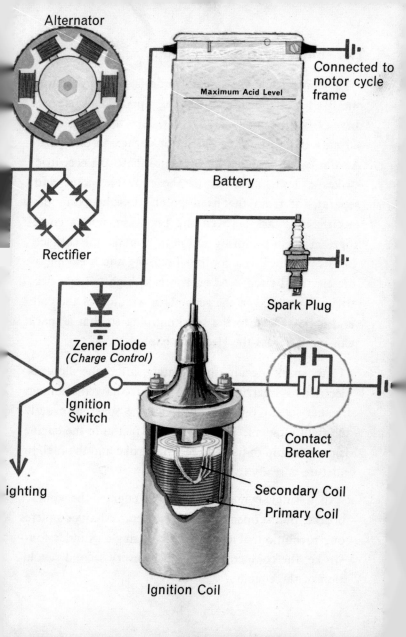

Alternator

Battery

Maximum Acid Level

Connected to
motor cycle
frame

Rectifier

Spark Plug

Zener Diode
(Charge Control)

Ignition
Switch

ighting

Contact
Breaker

Secondary Coil

Primary Coil

Ignition Coil

The contact breaker and timing

The contact breaker assembly consists of two points, one fixed and the other movable, operated by a *cam* driven from the engine crankshaft. The cam is basically a round bar with an eccentric, or corner, in one part. As the cam is rotated by the crankshaft, the eccentric strikes a lever attached to the movable point and separates it from the fixed point, thus breaking the electrical contact between the two. The points come together again by spring action to re-make the contact. In this way there is a continual making and breaking of the electrical circuit. At each break, high voltage electricity is induced in the secondary winding of the coil, and is passed on to the sparking plug so that a spark can jump across the electrode gap.

The spark occurs immediately after the flow of electricity is interrupted. It is essential to have the contact breaker set, or timed, to produce the spark at exactly the right moment. This is when the piston in the engine is near the top of its compression stroke and the fuel/air mixture is ready to be ignited.

In a single-cylinder two-stroke engine, the contact breaker points open every time the crankshaft completes one revolution. If the engine is a single-cylinder four-stroke, the contact breaker opens every second revolution of the engine.

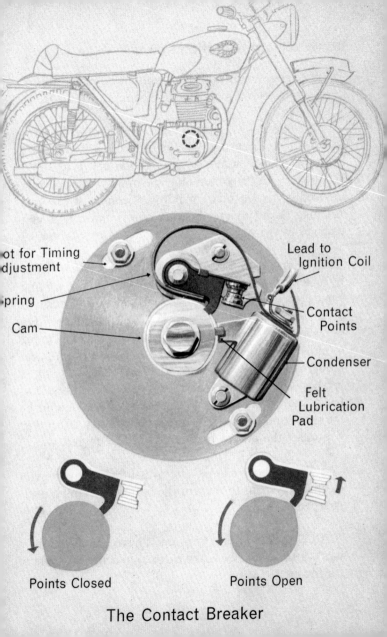

ot for Timing
djustment

pring

Cam

Lead to
Ignition Coil

Contact
Points

Condenser

Felt
Lubrication
Pad

Points Closed

Points Open

The Contact Breaker

Completing the ignition system

Although we have now dealt with the main features of the ignition, the information is not quite complete.

A *condenser* is connected across the contact breaker points, firstly to ensure that the breaking of the current in the primary winding of the ignition coil is as rapid as possible, thereby enabling maximum voltage to be induced in the secondary winding. Secondly, it prevents sparking at the contact breaker points and consequent damage to the points.

Some machines have a small lever on the handlebar by which the ignition timing can be varied to suit varying engine speeds. The spark can be *advanced* (made to occur sooner), or *retarded* (delayed a little longer). On other machines no lever is fitted. In this event the timing is either fixed at an average setting or, as on most modern motor cycles, is varied automatically by a mechanism within the contact breaker assembly. The faster the engine speed, the more advanced should be the spark and vice versa. Too much variation either way will upset the proper functioning of the engine.

A *Zener Diode charge control* is fitted to twelve-volt electrical systems to prevent the battery becoming over-charged.

All electrical installations must have a connection to earth. In a motor cycle the earth connection is made to the frame.

Automatic Advance/Retard

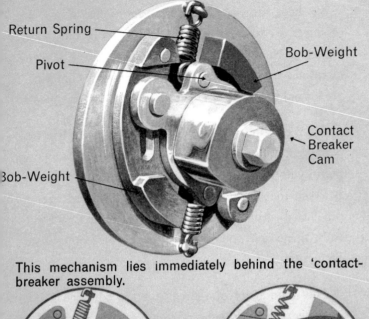

Return Spring

Pivot

Bob-Weight

Bob-Weight

Contact Breaker Cam

This mechanism lies immediately behind the 'contact-breaker assembly.

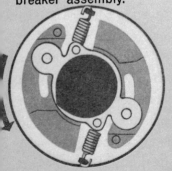

Low Speed

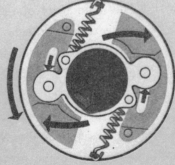

High Speed

As the engine revolutions increase, centrifugal force carries the bob-weights outwards, progressively turning the cam into the direction of rotation, thus *advancing the ignition.*

The fuel system and carburettor

We have now learned how the ignition system produces a spark between the electrodes of the sparking plug. Next we must find out how the other two essentials—petrol and air (the combustion mixture)—are brought into the engine to be ignited by the spark.

The fuel system consists of a tank, into which petrol is poured, and a *carburettor* which is a device for mixing petrol with air and passing the mixture into the engine. Between the tank and the carburettor is a connecting pipe fitted with a tap. This enables the main fuel supply to be turned off when the motor cycle or scooter is not being used.

The main body of the carburettor contains a *float chamber* which provides a small reserve of petrol to ensure a constant and controlled supply of fuel into the engine. There is a hollow *float* in the chamber and a needle valve in the supply pipe at the top. As the chamber fills with petrol from the tank, the float rises until it touches the needle. When this happens, the valve closes the pipe and prevents more petrol from flowing into the chamber. As petrol is used and the level in the chamber falls, the float comes away from the valve which then opens to allow more petrol to flow in.

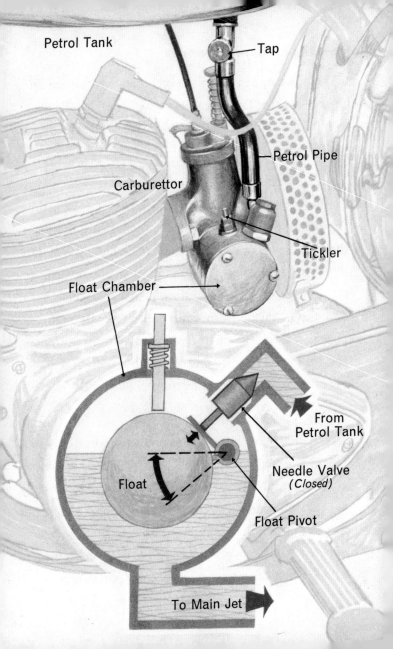

Petrol Tank

Tap

Petrol Pipe

Carburettor

Tickler

Float Chamber

From
Petrol Tank

Float

Needle Valve
(Closed)

Float Pivot

To Main Jet

How the carburettor works

The other main part of the carburettor is the *venturi*, or air inlet tube. This is connected with the float chamber by a thin pipe at the end of which is a nozzle known as the *main jet*.

Air from the atmosphere is drawn through the venturi by the sucking action of the piston on the induction stroke (see page 28). At the same time, petrol is sucked through the main jet which converts the liquid fuel into tiny droplets and passes it into the air stream in the form of a fine mist. The combustion mixture of petrol mist and air is then drawn into the engine through the *induction pipe*. The mixture normally consists of about fourteen parts of air to one of petrol. If there is a higher proportion of petrol, the mixture is said to be 'rich'. A higher proportion of air gives a 'weak' mixture.

The flow of air into the carburettor is controlled by a cylindrical *throttle slide* which moves across the throat of the venturi and, in the closed position, virtually blocks off the air passage. In this position, the supply of petrol through the main jet is also restricted by a long, tapered needle valve attached to the base of the throttle slide, which fits into the jet hole and partially closes it.

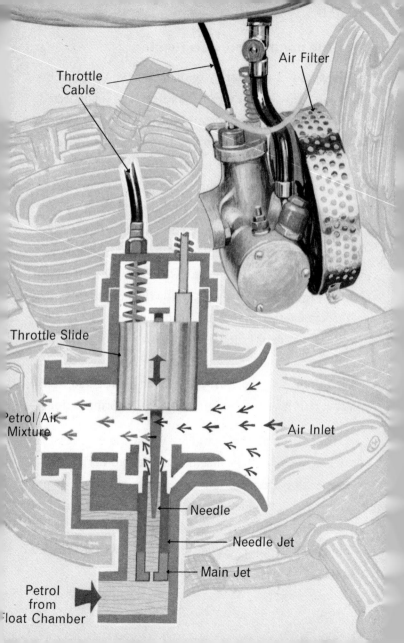

Throttle
Cable

Air Filter

Throttle Slide

Petrol/Air
Mixture

Air Inlet

Needle

Needle Jet

Main Jet

Petrol
from
Float Chamber

Throttle control and slow running

The speed of a motor cycle or scooter is regulated by the twist-grip control on the handlebar. It is connected by a wire cable to the throttle slide in the carburettor. When the twist-grip is rotated toward the rider, it pulls on the cable which in turn lifts the throttle slide. This action opens the throttle and allows air to be sucked in through the venturi by the movement of the piston. While this is happening the needle valve is being withdrawn from the needle jet to maintain the correct proportion of petrol to air. The extra air and petrol cause the engine to run faster. The further the twist-grip is rotated, the more the throttle opens; a greater volume of petrol and air is drawn into the engine and burnt, and a higher engine speed is achieved. When released, the twist-grip, throttle slide and needle valve return to the closed positions by spring action.

That is for normal running. When the engine is just 'ticking over' with the machine at rest, another jet, known as the 'slow-running' jet, comes into operation. It provides a small independent supply of petrol and air while the throttle is closed. The air supply can be adjusted by an external screw to give the required engine tick-over speed.

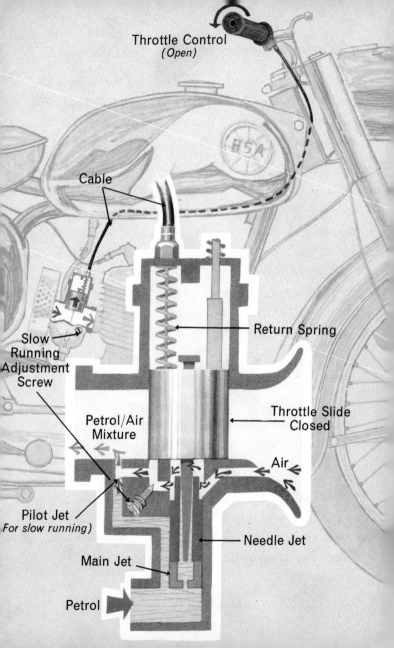

Throttle Control
(Open)

Cable

Slow Running Adjustment Screw

Return Spring

Petrol/Air Mixture

Throttle Slide Closed

Air

Pilot Jet
For slow running)

Needle Jet

Main Jet

Petrol

The piston, connecting rod and crankshaft

In previous chapters it has been explained how the engine is supplied with electricity, petrol and air. We now come to the chief mechanical components of the engine itself.

A single-cylinder engine has one cylinder into which is fitted a *piston*. The cylinder is really a vertical tube blocked off at the top end by the *cylinder head* into which the sparking plug is screwed. The piston fits comfortably within the cylinder and is able to slide up and down, each up or down movement being known as a stroke. Spring rings are fitted around the upper part of the piston, to exert pressure against the cylinder walls and provide a gas-tight and oil-tight seal.

The piston is joined to a *connecting rod* by a *gudgeon pin*. This joint is at the *little end*. The lower end of the connecting rod is attached to the *crankshaft* at the *big end*, by the *big end bearing*. The crankshaft is so designed that it revolves as the piston moves up and down.

The operation of the piston, connecting rod and crankshaft is rather like the movement of one of your legs when you ride a bicycle. You can imagine your knee as the piston pushing downward through your leg (the connecting rod) to the pedal and crank (the crankshaft).

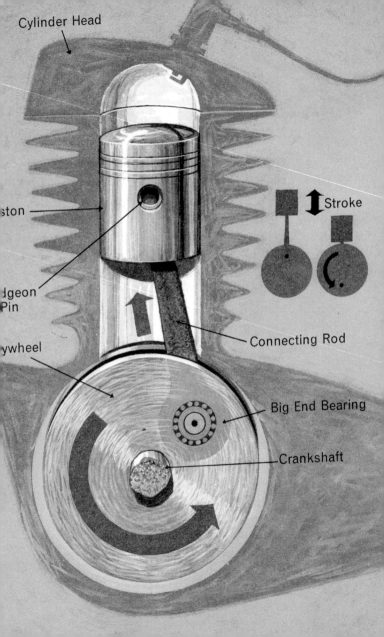

Cylinder Head

Piston

Gudgeon
Pin

Flywheel

Stroke

Connecting Rod

Big End Bearing

Crankshaft

Two-stroke and four-stroke engines

Before describing, in the next three pages, the actual operation of the engine, it is necessary to understand clearly what is meant by the terms 'two-stroke' and 'four-stroke'.

Many lightweight motor cycles and scooters are powered by a two-stroke engine. This means that the operating and firing sequence of the engine is completed in two strokes of the piston, one up and one down. During this time the crankshaft revolves once. The cylinder walls have three holes, or *ports*; one is the inlet port through which the combustion mixture enters the cylinder, the second is the transfer port and the third is the exhaust port through which the exhaust gases are expelled after combustion.

In the four-stroke system it takes four strokes of the piston to complete the operating sequence—two up strokes and two down strokes. Instead of ports in the cylinder walls, this type of engine is fitted with inlet and exhaust valves which are opened and closed by the action of cams on a *camshaft*. The camshaft can be either chain- or gear-driven from the crankshaft at half the crankshaft speed. The operating sequence is thus completed in two revolutions of the crankshaft.

Between each power stroke the crankshaft is kept revolving by means of *flywheels* attached to the centre of the crankshaft.

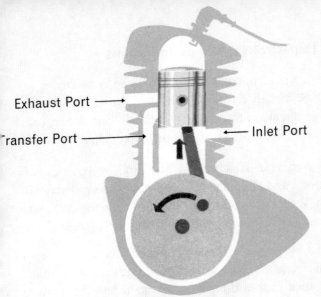

Two-Stroke Engine

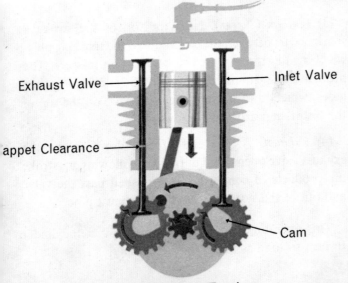

Four-Stroke Engine

The four-stroke cycle of operations

The cycle of operations for the four-stroke engine is easier to visualise than that of the two-stroke as the various stages are more clearly defined—one stroke, one operation. We will take the four-stroke first:

(1) *Induction*. This begins with the piston at the top of its stroke and the inlet valve open. As the piston goes down, it sucks the petrol/air mixture from the carburettor past the open inlet valve and into the cylinder.

(2) *Compression*. When the piston has completed its down stroke, the inlet valve closes. The revolving crankshaft then pushes the piston up again and the mixture now in the cylinder is compressed upward into the *combustion chamber*.

(3) *Ignition* (*Power*). Near the top of the stroke a spark occurs between the electrodes of the sparking plug, which ignites the compressed combustion mixture. The heat from the explosion causes terrific expansion of the gases, which in turn exerts great pressure on the top of the piston and drives it downward.

(4) *Exhaust*. At the end of this down stroke the exhaust valve opens, and during the following up stroke the products of combustion are pushed past the valve and out of the system through the exhaust pipe.

This operating sequence is repeated in each cylinder in turn so long as the engine is running.

Induction Stroke
Piston going down

Compression Stroke
Piston going up

Power Stroke
Piston going down

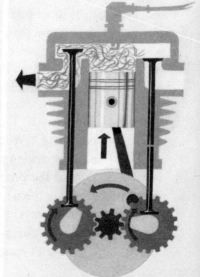

Exhaust Stroke
Piston going up

The two-stroke cycle of operations

In this type of engine, the four stages of the operating sequence have to be completed in only one revolution of the crankshaft, or two strokes of the piston. This means that two stages must be carried out at the same time during each stroke. The piston, cylinder, and the area in which the crankshaft revolves (the *crankcase*), are so designed that while one operation is taking place above the piston, another operation is occurring below it. Thus we get induction (below the piston) and compression (above the piston) occurring together, whilst ignition is followed immediately by exhaust. This is how it works.

(1) *Induction/Compression*. As the piston moves up the cylinder, it uncovers and opens the inlet port. The petrol/air mixture from the carburettor is sucked in below the piston and enters the crankcase. While this is going on, the previous charge of combustion mixture is being compressed at the top of the cylinder above the piston.

(2) *Ignition/exhaust*. When the piston nears the top of its stroke, the sparking plug sparks and the force of combustion drives the piston downwards. As it travels down it compresses the new charge of petrol and air in the crankcase. It passes the inlet port again and shuts it. Further down it uncovers the exhaust port through which the burnt gases escape from the engine.

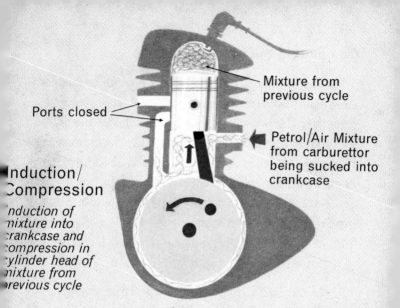

Mixture from
previous cycle

Ports closed

Petrol/Air Mixture
from carburettor
being sucked into
crankcase

Induction/
Compression

*Induction of
mixture into
crankcase and
compression in
cylinder head of
mixture from
previous cycle*

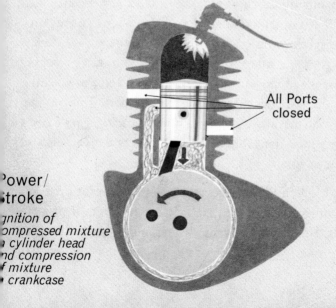

All Ports
closed

Power/
Stroke

*Ignition of
compressed mixture
in cylinder head
and compression
of mixture
in crankcase*

Completing the two-stroke cycle

Just before the piston reaches the bottom of its down stroke it uncovers a third port—the *transfer port*—leading to the *transfer passage*. Through this the petrol/air mixture that has been compressed in the crankcase is transferred to the top of the cylinder, ready to be re-compressed for ignition when the revolving crankshaft sends the piston up again. And so the whole process is repeated at enormously high speed during every revolution of the crankshaft. At maximum revs. it can be over ten thousand times a minute.

An interesting feature of two-stroke engine construction is the fact that although the burnt gases and the unburnt mixture are in the cylinder at the same time, they do not intermix. The top of the piston and the ports are specially designed so that the new mixture entering the cylinder above the piston, via the transfer passage, is made to swirl in such a way that it helps to push the burnt gases out through the exhaust port. This pushing out of the waste gases is known as *scavenging*. It is a very important function which affects the efficiency of the engine.

Modern four-stroke and two-stroke motor cycle and scooter engines are extremely efficient and, if properly used, should give many thousands of miles of good service.

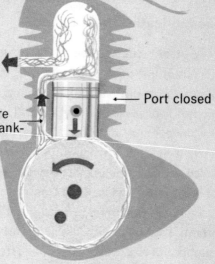

Expanding burnt gas escapes via exhaust, assisted by flow of new mixture

Port closed

ompressed mixture ansferred from crank-ase to cylinder

Exhaust and Transfer

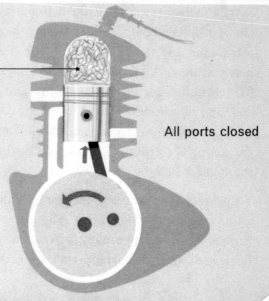

Mixture from crankcase

All ports closed

Induction and Compression

Engine lubrication and cooling

In two-stroke engines, oil to lubricate the moving parts is put into the fuel tank with the petrol. The oil is drawn into the engine, via the carburettor, with the petrol and air and is dispersed around the cylinder and crankcase by the combustion mixture. Thus, each charge of combustion mixture carries with it a small quantity of oil which reduces friction between the working parts before being burnt and expelled from the engine with the exhaust gases. The correct proportion of oil to petrol is important. Too much oil is liable to dirty the sparking plug points and create excessive smoke from the exhaust pipe, whilst too little may cause friction and wear.

With four-stroke engines, the petrol and oil are contained in different parts of the machine: the petrol in the petrol tank and the oil in the oil-tank. Petrol is used purely as the fuel, and the oil provides separate, pump-fed lubrication for pistons and valve gear, crankshaft and big-end bearings. There are two pumps, one force-feeding and the other pumping back to the tank from the sump. The piston is lubricated by oil splashed up the cylinder bore by the flywheels.

Engine cooling is carried out simply by the passage of air around the cylinder casing. The casing is finned to provide the maximum cooling surface. An air circulating fan is used when the engine is enclosed within covers.

Four Stroke Engine Lubrication

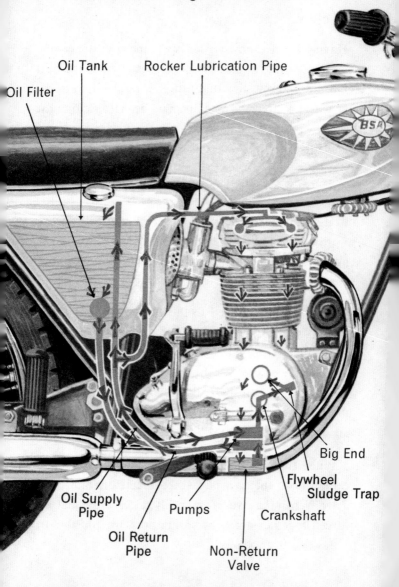

Oil Filter

Oil Tank

Rocker Lubrication Pipe

BSA

Big End

Oil Supply Pipe

Pumps

Oil Return Pipe

Flywheel Sludge Trap

Crankshaft

Non-Return Valve

The clutch

Having learned how power is produced in the engine of a motor cycle or scooter, we can pass on to the next stage and find out how that power is transmitted to the rear wheel so that the machine may be driven along the road. There are three main sections we have to consider: *clutch*, *gearbox* and *transmission drive*.

The various gears in the gearbox cannot be engaged whilst the power from the engine is being transmitted through them. The purpose of the clutch, therefore, is to provide a method of disconnecting the drive for gear engagement and re-connecting it when the appropriate gear has been selected.

A flat disc is attached to the gearbox mainshaft and revolves with it. A clutch plate, consisting of another metal plate faced with a high-friction material, is held tightly against the disc by a spring-operated pressure plate. As the mainshaft disc revolves, the clutch plate also revolves and it is simply the pressure of one against the other that provides the drive from engine to gearbox.

When the clutch lever on the handlebar is pulled, a cable draws the two plates apart and disconnects the drive. When the lever is smoothly released the plates are forced together again by spring pressure and the drive is taken up once more.

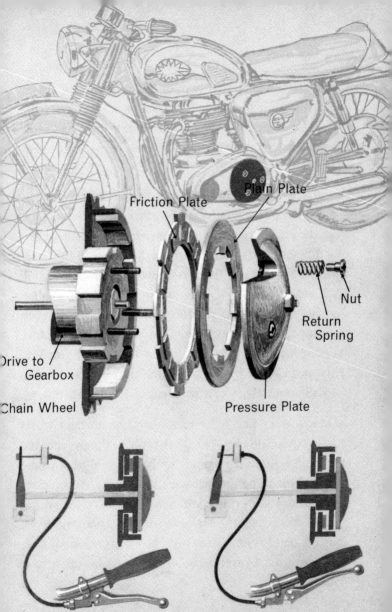

Plain Plate

Friction Plate

Nut

Return Spring

Drive to Gearbox

Chain Wheel

Pressure Plate

Engaged

Disengaged

The gearbox

The gearbox is usually built into the engine crankcase or transmission housing and contains several pairs of gears. Their purpose is to enable the most efficient engine speed to be obtained relative to the speed required at the back wheel.

The gears are of varying sizes and so arranged that certain pairs can be selected to make one gear, driven from the engine via the clutch, engage with another gear of a different size which transmits the power to the back wheel. This changes the *ratio* between the engine and back wheel speeds. If a larger gear drives a smaller one, a high ratio is produced whilst a smaller gear driving a larger one results in a low ratio. Most modern machines are fitted with a four-speed gearbox. This means that by operating the gear selector pedal, four different ratios can be engaged in the gearbox.

In low ratio, the engine runs fast while the back wheel rotates quite slowly. As higher ratio gears are engaged the engine speed drops but the back wheel goes round faster. Engine power increases with speed (revolutions per minute). Low ratios are therefore used when greater power is needed to start off from rest, to accelerate quickly and to climb steep hills. Normal cruising is done in high gear. Correct gear selection is a vital part of riding.

Change up
432

321
Change down

(On some machines these
positions are reversed)

Detail of Sliding Dog
When 'dog' is engaged
free gear rotates with shaft.

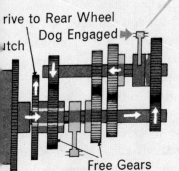

Drive to Rear Wheel
Dog Engaged
Clutch

Free Gears

First Gear

Dog Engaged

Fixed Gears

Second Gear

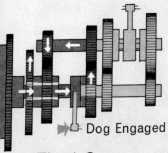

Third Gear

Dog Engaged

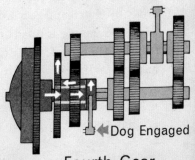

Fourth Gear

Dog Engaged

The transmission drive

The transmission system, of which the clutch and gearbox are parts, is completed by the drive which connects the gearbox with the back wheel and causes it to rotate.

On a bicycle, power is generated by the cyclist pushing the pedals round and round. The cogged wheel attached to the pedal cranks, and going round with them, is connected to the back wheel by a chain. As the pedals rotate, the back wheel rotates. The same sort of system is adopted for most motor cycles and scooters. A very much stronger chain than that used for the ordinary bicycle is fitted to motorised machines. It is connected between the driven, or output, shaft and cog of the gearbox and a cogged wheel fitted to the back wheel.

Although the chain is the most common form of transmission drive, other methods can be used, each manufacturer choosing the most suitable type for his particular design of machine. Sometimes the engine is mounted alongside the back wheel and there is a direct drive, by clutch and gearbox, between one and the other. With the engine located in its more usual position in front of the wheel, belt drive and shaft drive are alternatives to the chain drive method.

Whichever system is used the object is to provide a reliable transfer of power to the back wheel.

Primary Chain   Clutch and Gearbox   Rear Chain

Conventional Transmission

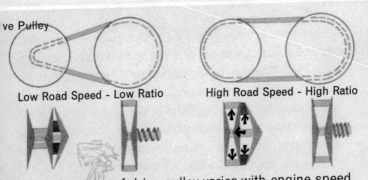

ve Pulley

Low Road Speed - Low Ratio   High Road Speed - High Ratio

(Effective) Diameter of drive pulley varies with engine speed due to centrifugal force

Automatic Pulley and Belt Transmission

The brakes

All motor cycles and scooters have two brakes, one for the front wheel and one for the back wheel. The front brake is applied by a hand lever on the handlebar, and the rear by means of a pedal. The vast majority of machines are fitted with drum brakes, although disc brakes are now used on one or two models.

Drum brakes are of the internal expanding type in which two shoes, with friction linings attached to them, are forced, or expanded, against the inside of a drum at each wheel. The drum revolves with the wheel and the grip between the shoes and the drum causes the braking action.

The shoes are supported on a backplate by a pivot at one end and a cam at the other. The cam is attached to a lever on the outside of the backplate which is connected to the handlebar control or pedal by either a cable or a metal rod. Application of the brakes pulls the cable or rod and actuates the lever which in turn rotates the cam. This forces the shoes against the drum. The harder the brakes are applied the further the cam rotates and the greater will be the pressure between shoes and drum. When the brakes are released, springs pull the shoes away from the drum again.

Disc brakes work by the pressure of pads of special material against a revolving steel disc.

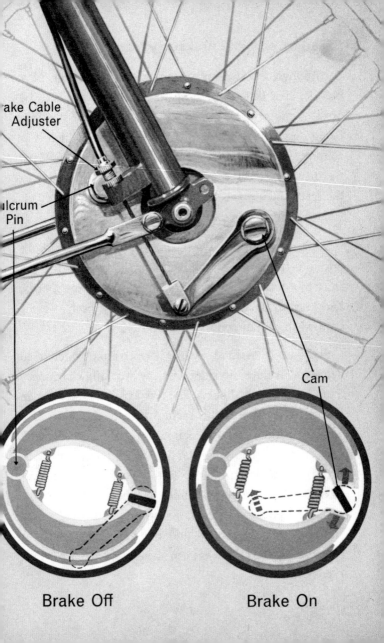

Brake Cable
Adjuster

Fulcrum
Pin

Cam

Brake Off   Brake On

Steering, stability and suspension

Although the steering system is similar to that of a bicycle, very little turning of the handlebar needs to be done. A motor cycle or scooter is virtually self-steering, being designed to travel in the direction in which it is leaning. If the rider wishes to turn to the right he leans the machine to the right. To turn to the left he leans to the left. The steering automatically centres itself again when the upright position is resumed.

Steering is combined with stability and both are built into the machine. No actual effort is needed for the rider to maintain his balance, except at very low speeds, and turning is done almost entirely by body weight applied in one direction or the other.

Stability is assisted by the suspension, which also helps to insulate the rider and the working machinery from bumps and shocks. The suspension system is in two parts. Firstly, it has springs to provide a soft ride and allow the wheels to follow the road surface. Coil springs are normally used and they are often contained within a telescopic casing. But springs by themselves have too much natural bounce, so the suspension also includes shock absorbers, or spring dampers, which smoothly restrict the up and down movement of the springs. Shock absorbers are usually of the hydraulic type.

Oil

Front Suspension

Hints on safe riding

Controlling the machine, so that it works for and not against you, is an all-important requirement in motor cycling and scootering. Here are a few hints on how to handle it safely and sympathetically.

When possible, only brake when the machine is upright and running straight. Use both brakes, the front a moment before the rear.

If you must brake on a bend, use the rear brake only. The front brake should only be used in good conditions, never on loose or slippery surfaces.

Cornering should be done at the right speed in the right gear. Do not accelerate on the bend itself, but you may accelerate gently out of it.

Operate the clutch progressively and do not let the lever flip out of your hand when releasing it.

Use the gearbox. Change down early so that you can accelerate briskly to overtake slow-moving traffic, and can let the engine help in braking if you have to stop.

Never ride at maximum speed for more than a minute or two at a time. Discover the machine's comfortable cruising speed and use it.

Do not allow the engine to labour in too high a gear. This can cause more damage than over-revving it.

Adopt a comfortable position in the saddle and wear suitable clothing. Always wear a safety helmet.

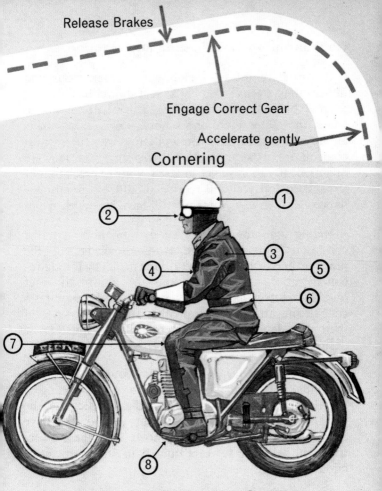

Release Brakes

Engage Correct Gear

Accelerate gently

Cornering

Safety and Comfort in the Saddle

Safety helmet white for
night driving

Non-splinter goggles

Wind and rain-proof clothing

Straight forearm and
slightly angled upper arm

5 Slight forward lean to body

6 Reflective material on
gloves and belt

7 Knees at right angle and
against tank

8 Foot poised over brake
pedal

Concentration, anticipation and reaction

If you have followed closely the descriptions and illustrations given in this book, you should have gained a good basic knowledge of the general principles on which the motor cycle and scooter work. If you have already learned to ride, you will know why the various controls are necessary and what happens when they are operated. If you have yet to learn, your appreciation of the instruction you will receive should be greatly enhanced. Either way your time will have been well spent.

Riding a motor cycle or scooter in modern traffic conditions demands more than knowledge of the practical and technical aspects of the machine. It requires concentration, anticipation and the ability to react quickly to any situation that develops. It also requires a considerate attitude toward other road users—even if their attitude toward you sometimes leaves much to be desired.

Concentrate your attention on your own riding; handling your machine properly and positioning it correctly in relation to other traffic. Anticipate the possible actions of others so that you always have ample time to make your own move. Both these objectives will help you to react quickly in any given set of circumstances.

Avoid showing-off. If you are proficient, the skill you show in every aspect of riding will immediately become obvious.

Be courteous yourself and always acknowledge the courtesy of others.

"I intend to pull in or turn to my left"

"I intend to pull out or turn to my right"

"I intend to slow down or stop"

...orrect distance from vehicle in ...ont. Good safety margin and ...ew of the road ahead.

...o close. No safety margin and ...or visibility.

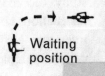
Waiting position

Signal

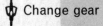
Change gear

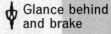
Glance behind and brake

Glance behind and signal

(Turning Right)

Hints on maintenance

A good rider deserves a good machine, but a machine will only remain good so long as it is properly cared for. Motor cycles and scooters bought second-hand, and those which have had long periods of use, require special attention.

The first duty on acquiring a machine, therefore, is to study the maker's handbook and carry out all the instructions contained in it at the recommended mileage intervals. Neglect of any component may result in expensive repair work or replacement. It may also be dangerous if, for instance, the brakes should fail for any reason. Here are some points to which particular attention should be paid.

Check oil levels and top up as necessary. Make sure the lights are working efficiently—back as well as front. Brake, clutch and throttle cables need a trace of oil; if neglected they will rust and break. Tyres must always be in good condition and at the recommended pressures; worn tyres are dangerous. Watch for excessive wear, stretch or misalignment of driving chains. Do not allow wear in steering head or wheel bearings to go unattended.

Keep your machine clean. Not only will this show that you are a proud owner, it will also enable you to discover any loose nuts or bolts and other faults as soon as they occur.

Routine Maintenance

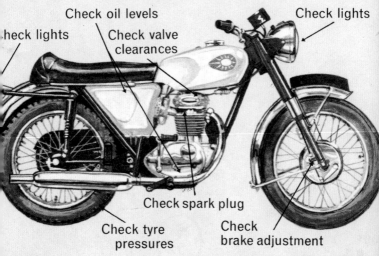

Check oil levels

Check valve clearances

heck lights

Check lights

Check spark plug

Check tyre pressures

Check brake adjustment

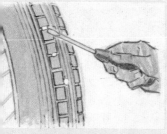

move stones embedded in e tread

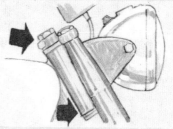

Check for wear in steering head bearings

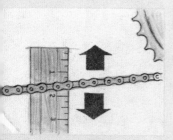

heck driving chains

Check for wear in wheel bearings

Series 654
A Ladybird 'How it works' Book